Glitter
and sparkle

This edition published in 2015
By SpiceBox™
12171 Horseshoe Way
Richmond, BC
Canada V7A 4V4

First published in 2014
Copyright © SpiceBox™ 2014

ISBN 10: 1-77132-313-2
ISBN 13: 978-1-77132-313-0

CEO & Publisher: Ben Lotfi
Editorial: Ania Jaraczewski
Creative Director: Garett Chan
Art Director: Christine Covert
Design & Layout: Kimberly Ang
Photography: Charmaine Muzyka
Production: James Badger, Mell D'Clute
Sourcing: Janny Lam, Sherry Xie

Special thanks to our model, Chelsea Mellish

For more SpiceBox products and information, visit our website:
www.spiceboxbooks.com

Manufactured in China

3 5 7 9 10 8 6 4

Contents

JUST ADD GLITTER

Make it Shine!

Have fun making glamorous, shimmery decorations and accessories! Try out fabulous crafts like sparkly modeling clay, glitter bugs and a shiny tiara. Then scrounge through your closet and drawers and pick out some shoes, bags, sunglasses and other old and forgotten stuff, and make it new again with a few sparkles. There's no limit to what you can glam up with a touch of glitter!

Tools & Materials

Glitter craft sheets

These shimmery stick-on foam sheets are an easy, non-messy way of crafting with glitter. Just cut out the shapes you want, peel off the backing and stick them on!

Glue

Plain white craft glue is all you need for your crafting. Just make sure you use the kind that dries clear.

Masking tape

This type of tape is easy to peel away without causing damage or leaving sticky gunk behind. It's perfect for covering any areas that you don't want to glitter, and for creating straight lines and borders.

Paintbrush

Using a paintbrush will make it easier to apply glue exactly where you want it and create designs to sprinkle your sparkles onto.

Paper towels, cloths

Keep paper towels or damp cloths on hand to clean up any spills, splashes and stray glue.

Glitter!

Of course this will be the number 1 ingredient in your crafting adventures. Experiment with different colors and kinds of loose glitter and glitter glue. You can create all sorts of designs and effects!

Recipe

Decoupage Glue

For many of the projects in this book it will help to have a type of glue that you can just spread on with a paintbrush. This glue is super quick and easy to make just using craft glue and water!

What you need:

- small jar or container with a tight lid
- white craft glue
- water

How to make it:

1. Measure out ¼ cup white glue and pour it into your jar.

2. Next add 2 tablespoons of water to the jar.

3. Stir the water and glue together until they are well mixed.

4. When you're not using your glue, just screw the lid on and it will be ready for your next crafting session!

You may want to ask an adult to help you!

Hints & Tips

Glitter, glitter everywhere

Glitter gets into everything! It will end up on your clothes, your floor and your friends. To lessen the danger of glittering up furniture and the family pet, make sure to always work over a layer of newspaper. Use an upside-down shoebox lid to catch leftover glitter so you can reuse it later.

Be creative

You can make the projects in this book exactly as they're shown, but wouldn't it be fun to use the ideas as inspiration and make your own awesome designs? Use your imagination!

Upcycle it!

Glittering up old shoes, sunglasses and other accessories is a great way to give old things new life. Rummage through your closet and see if you have some stuff you don't wear anymore that could use a sparkly style update.

Sparkle Fish Photo Frame

Brighten up your room with your own hand-painted glittery decor!

What you need:

- fish frame from kit
- decoupage glue (see p. 8)
- paintbrush
- colorful sequins
- toothpicks
- tape

How to make it:

1. Look inside your kit and find the fish-shaped photo frame.

2. You'll be putting your sequin design on the front part of the fish, the one with the hole. Pick one section of the fish and use a paintbrush to cover it with a layer of decoupage glue.

3. Using a toothpick, pick up the sequins one by one and stick them down onto the glue. Keep going until the entire glued area is covered in sequins.

4. Spread glue onto another part of your fish and cover it with sequins like before. Doesn't it look like your fish has sparkly scales?

5. Stick on a pretty craft gem for the eye, then leave the fish to dry for a few hours.

6. Find a nice photo that you want to put in your shimmery frame. Trim the photo and arrange it so that it fits nicely in the circle, then tape it in place. Glue on the back piece of the frame to hide the back of the photo, and you're finished. What a bright idea for a gift!

Tip:
Use the tiara design as a template, and trace it onto paper so you can make tiaras for all your friends. Then host a fancy princess-themed party!

Twinkling Tiara

Be a princess for a day with a glamorous tiara you've made yourself!

What you need:

- tiara design sheet from kit
- glitter glue
- toothpick
- mini hole punch or awl (optional)
- feathers, beads, sequins (optional)
- glue or clear tape

How to make it:

1. Find the tiara design sheet in your kit. Punch out the tiara from the backing. Make sure you punch out all the little pieces as well.

2. Use your glitter glue to decorate the pattern on the tiara. It might help to use a toothpick to spread the glitter glue and fill in the edges neatly.

3. If you want your tiara to have decorative edges, you can use a mini hole punch or an awl to make little holes all along the top and bottom.

4. You can also make your tiara extra fancy by gluing on feathers, beads, sequins or other flashy decorations. Show off your royal personality!

5. Once your tiara looks just the way you want, glue or tape the ends together so you can wear it. Be sure to act like a princess, to match your fairy-tale look!

Bejeweled Bookmarks

Don't let your favorite books get dog-eared!
Keep your place with these fabulous bookmarks.

What you need:

- glitter craft foam
- scissors
- large paper clip
- craft glue
- craft gem or button
- pen or marker

How to make it:

1. Draw two matching flower or heart shapes onto the back of a glitter foam sheet. You can use the templates at the back of the book for your flowers.

2. Cut the shapes out with a pair of scissors.

3. If the foam has a sticky backing, just peel the paper off and place the top part of your paper clip onto the sticky side. If your foam has no sticky side, glue the paper clip down with craft glue. Make sure that you don't stick down the end of the paper clip that you will use to clip the bookmark onto your page!

4. Now take your second shape and stick it, or glue it, onto the back of the first shape, over the paper clip. Make sure the glitter side is facing out.

5. Pick out a button or craft gem in a matching color and use craft glue to stick it onto the middle of your flower. You can also layer your embellishments and glue a gem on top of a button for added sparkle!

6. Let your bookmark dry completely before clipping it into your latest read.

Glitter Clay

Use this sparkly clay like Play-Doh. Have fun molding and shaping it, then put it into a plastic container or a zippered plastic bag to keep it from drying out. Be creative and make all kinds of cool, glittery things!

What you need:

- 4 cups all-purpose white flour
- 1 cup table salt
- ½ cup cream of tartar
- 4 cups water
- ¼ cup vegetable oil
- pair of kitchen gloves
- food coloring in different colors
- loose glitter in different colors
- parchment paper

How to make it:

1. Ask an adult to help you make your clay. In a large pot, mix together the flour, salt and cream of tartar. Stir in the water and oil.

2. Stir the ingredients until the mixture is smooth and free of lumps. You can use an electric mixer on a low setting.

3. Place the pot on the stove and turn the heat to medium. Stir constantly as it cooks and the mixture starts to thicken. You might need to ask someone to lend you a hand or two when your arm gets tired!

4. When the mixture is very thick, take it off from the heat. Stir the dough a few more times until the lumps are all gone.

5. Place some parchment paper down on the counter and turn the pot over so the dough slides onto the paper. It will be warm and soft and smooth to the touch.

6. Roll the dough into a log shape. Ask an adult to cut the dough into five or six pieces so that you can make different colors of clay.

7. Put on a pair of kitchen gloves, or your hands might turn multicolored! Take one of your clay lumps and add several drops of food coloring to it. Kneed the color into the clay until it's mixed in well. Add more food coloring if you want the color to be darker.

8. Now for the really fun part! Sprinkle some glitter into the clay. Pick a glitter that has large sparkles so that it stands out. It's also fun to use glitter that has little stars or hearts for a really cool effect.

9. Add different colors and glitter to the rest of your clay lumps, so you have a rainbow of options to choose from!

Party Hairbands

Make your own hairbands to match your favorite outfits so you can go from school style to party style in seconds!

What you need:

- glitter foam sheets
- pen or marker
- scissors
- craft glue
- hairband
- felt or fabric (optional)

How to make it:

1. Pick out craft foam in colors that will match your hairband or an outfit you like.

2. Use a pen or marker to draw shapes and designs on the backside of the foam sheet. Think stars, hearts, flowers and butterflies! You can use the templates at the back of the book if you want.

3. Use scissors to cut out your foam shapes.

4. If you want to be extra crafty, cut out some felt or fabric to stick to the back of your foam shapes. If the foam has a sticky backing, all you need to do is peel off the paper and stick the foam onto the fabric. If the foam does not have a sticky backing, use some craft glue.

5. Cut a small strip of foam or fabric and use it to attach each shape to your hairband. Simply dot glue on either side of the strip, place the elastic across the middle, and stick your shape down on top.

Tip:

If you want to be really creative, you can make a bunch of paper shapes and then glue your letters onto the shapes so that each one has a nice backing.

Sparkly Sign

Make a pretty name sign for your room, or a fun party banner.

How to make it:

1. Decide what you want your banner to say. For example, you can create a banner with your name to hang on your bedroom door, or make one that says "Happy Birthday" for a party.

2. Draw big block letters onto colorful card stock or thick paper. Cut the letters out.

3. Use glitter glue to outline each letter and make it shine.

4. Squeeze out several dots of glue onto one of your letters and stick a sequin down on each glue dot. Repeat with the other letters.

5. To decorate your letter, you can make little shapes from card stock or glitter craft foam. Think flowers, stars and butterflies! Glitter up the shapes and glue them onto your letters. Let the letters dry.

6. Cut your ribbon into small pieces and dab glue onto the ends, then use a piece of ribbon to connect each letter to another. You can also glue the letters along one long piece of ribbon. Let the glue dry for a few hours, and then your banner will be ready for you to hang it up!

What you need:

- colored card stock
- scissors
- sequins
- glitter glue
- craft glue
- ribbon

Birds of Paradise Mobile

These birds of a feather shimmer and shine together!

What you need:

- colored paper
- scissors
- glitter glue
- craft glue
- small craft gems
- small hole punch
- string
- long dowel or stick

How to make it:

1. Use the templates on page 47 to trace out a bunch of birds onto bright, colorful paper. For each bird you will need a body piece and three wing pieces in different sizes.

2. Glue the largest wing piece onto your bird first, pointing up. Then glue down the second largest piece, overlapping a bit, and then glue on the smallest piece.

3. Glue a little craft gem onto the head of each bird for an eye, then let the glue dry.

4. Now have fun decorating your birds with glitter glue! Create any patterns and designs you like to make the birds and their wings pretty and shimmery. Leave the birds until the glitter glue has dried.

5. Punch a small hole into the top wing of each bird. Thread each bird onto a piece of string and tie a knot in the string so that the bird stays in place. Tie all the strings to the dowel and hang your fabulous mobile in your room, or anywhere that could use a bit of sparkle!

Tip:
Be creative and make your mobile with butterflies, tropical fish, flowers... even dinosaurs or spaceships!

Celebrity Sunglasses

Ask your mom or grandmother if they have any old frames that you can use for a glam, retro Hollywood look!

What you need:

- sunglasses (plastic frames work best)
- loose glitter
- decoupage glue (see p. 8)
- paintbrush
- craft gems

How to make it:

1. Use a paintbrush to spread a thick coat of decoupage glue over the areas you want to glitter. If you smudge glue onto the lenses, just wipe it away with a damp cloth so you don't end up seeing stars in your eyes!

2. Shake plenty of loose glitter over the glasses until the glue is completely covered and your design is all sparkly.

3. Set your sunglasses aside to dry for a couple of hours.

4. Once they've dried, tap the sunglasses gently on your work surface to shake off any extra glitter. Use a soft, clean paintbrush to brush away any stray sparkles off the lenses. If you want, add some craft gems for extra sparkle!

Cool!

Dazzling Rings

Nothing says stylish like a big, bold ring. It's just the thing to complete a uniquely awesome outfit.

What you need:

- adjustable ring
- loose glitter
- decoupage glue (see page 8)
- craft glue
- paintbrush
- button
- large craft gems

How to make it:

1. You can find adjustable rings in craft stores, or just use a piece of elastic or ribbon instead.

2. Using craft glue, stick a large button onto your ring and let it dry for a few hours.

3. Once the glue is dry, use a paintbrush to cover the button with decoupage glue.

4. Shake loose glitter over the glue until the area is completely sparkly.

5. Let the glue dry for a couple of hours.

6. Pick out a nice big craft gem to glue on top of the ring to bling it out. Glue the gem in the middle of the ring. Wow, what a fashion statement!

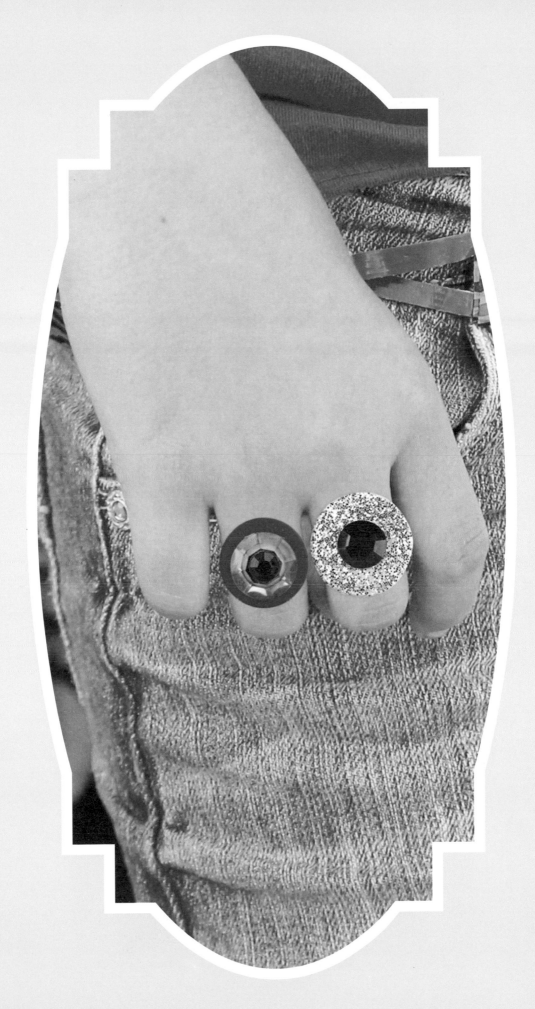

Tip:
You can also use a glitter craft foam shape with a hole punched through it to make a cool keychain. Use the templates at the back of the book.

Shimmery Key Caps

Personalize your house keys, bike lock keys and secret drawer keys with their own awesome glittery caps!

What you need:

- keys
- glitter foam sheet
- pen or marker
- scissors

How to make it:

1. Lay your key down on the non-shiny side of your sheet of craft foam. Use a pen or marker to trace around the top of the key. Move the key to another spot on the foam and trace around it again.

2. Cut both pieces out from the foam using scissors.

3. Peel off the paper backing and stick one piece on each side of the key. Now it will be so much easier to find your bright, shiny key if it goes missing!

Fancy Flowers

Any time of the year can be springtime when you make your very own flowers that shimmer in the sunshine.

What you need:

- glitter craft foam
- scissors
- craft glue
- pen or marker
- green pipe cleaner (optional)

How to make it:

1. Pick a sheet of glitter foam in a color you like.

2. Use a flower template from the back of the book to trace a flower shape onto the back of your glitter foam.

3. Draw a couple of leaves onto a sheet of green foam. You can also make a stem out of craft foam, or use green pipe cleaner.

4. Cut out all the pieces with a pair of scissors.

5. Use craft glue to glue the flower and leaves to your stem. Now make a few more flowers in different colors so you can gather them into a gorgeous bouquet!

Tip:
Wouldn't these lovely flowers make a fantastic gift for a friend or family member? Try the vase project on the next page to make it extra special!

Tip:

If you are using a small, wide-mouthed jar (like a mason jar), you can also use it as a great candle holder.

Amazing Vase

Upcycle a used jar or bottle into a wonderful mini vase, so you can brighten your room with flowers!

What you need:

- clean, empty glass jar, bottle or vase
- masking tape
- decoupage glue (see p. 8)
- loose glitter

How to make it:

1. Decide how much of your vase you want to cover in sparkles, and use masking tape to make a line all around the vase. Everything below this line will end up covered in glitter!

2. Use a paintbrush to cover the entire area below the tape with decoupage glue, except for the underside of the vase.

3. Shake loose glitter over the vase, or roll the vase in a pile of glitter to cover the part that you glued.

4. Let the vase dry for a few hours, then tap it against your work surface so that any extra glitter falls off. Now you have a beautiful flower vase that makes a perfect gift for a parent or teacher!

Glitter Easter Eggs

Forget shy pastels...
add some shine to your Easter egg designs!

What you need:

- white hard-boiled eggs
- plastic cups
- food coloring in different colors
- white vinegar
- soup spoons
- small container like a clean pudding cup
- empty egg carton

How to make it:

1. Set out a plastic cup for each color you want to make. Put about 20 drops of food coloring and 1 teaspoon of white vinegar into each cup. Ask an adult to pour some hot water into the cups without filling them up. There should still be room to fit an egg in each cup.

2. Carefully drop an egg into each color and let it sit for 10–15 minutes.

3. Lift the eggs out of the food coloring with a soup spoon. If you like the color of the egg, place it onto some paper towel to dry. If the color isn't bright enough, put the egg back into the food coloring for a few more minutes.

4. In the meantime, pour some decoupage glue into a small container like an empty, clean pudding or yogurt cup. Pour a good amount of loose glitter into another container.

5. Once your eggs are dry, dunk the bottom half of each egg into the glue and then into the glitter. Place the eggs upside down into the egg carton to dry. Even the Easter bunny will be jealous!

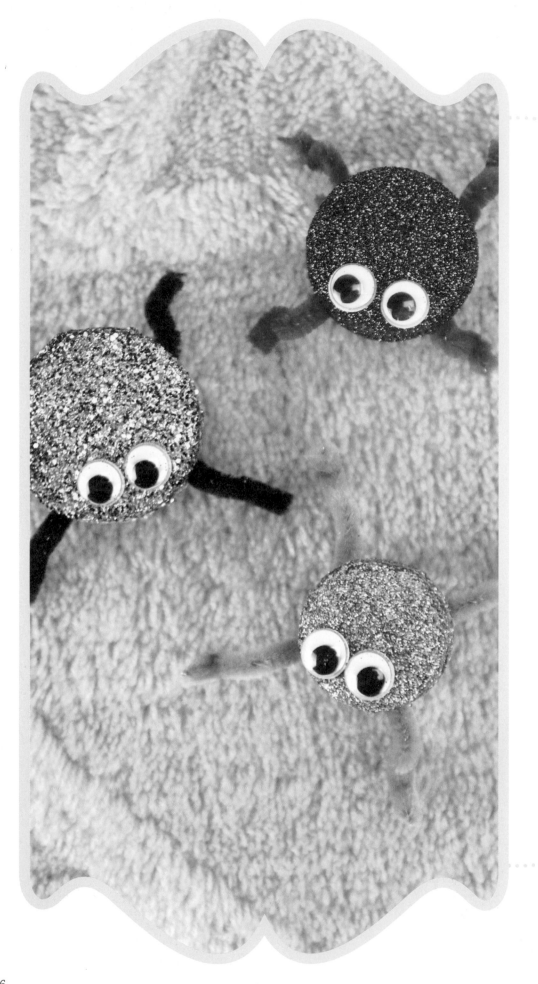

Shimmer Bugs

These cute little critters will make your day with their cheerful shine.

What you need:

- bottle caps
- loose glitter
- decoupage glue (see p. 8)
- googly eyes
- pipe cleaner

How to make it:

1. Make sure your bottle cap is clean and dry. Use a paintbrush to spread a layer of decoupage glue over the top and sides of the cap.

2. Sprinkle loose glitter over the glue until the cap is completely covered in sparkles.

3. Leave the cap to dry for a couple of hours, then glue two googly eyes on top.

4. While you wait for the cap to dry, you can make your bug's crawly little legs. Cut two pieces of pipe cleaner that are about 4 inches (10 cm) each.

5. Twist the pieces together in the middle so that they make an X shape. Now place your cap in the middle of the X and bend the legs all around the cap to make knees. Then bend the ends of the pipe cleaner to make little feet. Adorable!

Trinket Box

This little box is perfect for storing jewelry, or gifting tiny treasures to friends and family.

What you need:

- heart box design sheet from kit
- loose glitter or glitter glue
- decoupage glue (see p. 8)
- paintbrush

How to make it:

1. Find the sheet with the heart box design in your kit, and punch it out from the backing. Cut along the lines of the little "V" shape to create an opening for the clasp.

2. Use a paintbrush to spread decoupage glue on the smaller heart on the clasp, then shake some loose glitter over it. You can also use glitter glue to make some designs on the front of the box.

3. Leave the box flat and let it dry for a couple of hours.

4. Once it's dry, crease the paper sharply at the fold lines and fold it up so that your box has a top and a bottom, with panels going along the sides. Put glue on the tabs at the bottom of the heart and stick the tabs to the insides of the box. At the top of the heart, fit the two notches of the side panels together to close the box.

5. Fit the clasp into the opening on the front of the box and you're finished!

Tip:

Wouldn't it be cute to
put some little cinnamon
hearts or chocolates into
this box, and give someone
a Valentine's gift from
the heart?

Butterfly Wall Art

Make a beautiful 3D butterfly for your room!

What you need:

- paper box lid
- acrylic paint (optional)
- paintbrush
- loose glitter or glitter glue
- decoupage glue (see p. 8)
- scissors
- ruler
- pencil

How to make it:

1. You will need the lid from a paper gift box to make your "canvas." If you want to make the box lid a different color, you can paint over it with acrylic paint and leave it to dry.

2. In the meantime, you can glitter up your butterfly's wings! Trace the butterfly template at the back of the book onto a piece of stiff paper. Use glitter glue to add color and sparkle to the designs.

3. Let your butterfly dry, then cut it out.

4. Gently fold the butterfly's wings so that they will stick upward from the body (see photo).

5. Glue the middle of the butterfly onto the center of your canvas. If you need to, adjust and bend the wings so that they stick out from the canvas evenly.

6. Let your art dry flat on a table.

7. Ask an adult to help you hang your butterfly on your wall. You are a true artist!

Owl Wall Hanger

Keep your jewelry organized with this cute forest friend.

What you need:

- owl hanger pieces from kit
- craft glue
- glitter glue
- craft gems

How to make it:

1. Find the pieces for the owl hanger in your kit. You will have an owl piece and a backing piece.

2. Use glitter glue to decorate the owl's feathers and the designs on the branch. "Owl" you need is a few sparkles!

3. Take the backing piece and fold along all the crease lines. Glue the tab at the end of each folded section to the back of the owl and let it dry.

4. Ask an adult to help you hang the owl on your wall. The backing will make it stand out from the surface a bit so that you can hang light pieces of jewelry and other little treasures on the leaves.

Glittery Greetings

Brighten someone's day with a unique, sparkly card!

What you need:

- greeting cards from kit
- glitter glue
- googly eyes
- craft gems
- glitter gel pen (optional)

How to make it:

1. Find the greeting cards in your kit. You'll see that they have some designs printed on them for you.

2. Use glitter glue to make the designs on the cards all colorful and sparkly.

3. Add googly eyes, sequins or other decorations to make your cards even more fun. Be creative!

4. Write your greeting inside. For extra shimmer, use a glitter gel pen to create your message. Your card is sure to bring a smile to someone's face!

Paper Birdhouse

1. Find the birdhouse design sheet in your kit and punch out all the pieces from the backing.

2. Fold the tabs, sides and the bottom of the birdhouse in the direction shown by the arrows in the diagram. It should form a box shape with an open top.

3. Dot some glue on the tabs and stick the sides and the bottom together. Make sure the tabs are on the inside of the birdhouse.

4. Fold in the top like a milk carton and glue together the tabs at the top.

5. Glue on the roof and the little bird and flower pieces.

6. Decorate your birdhouse with glitter glue!

Templates

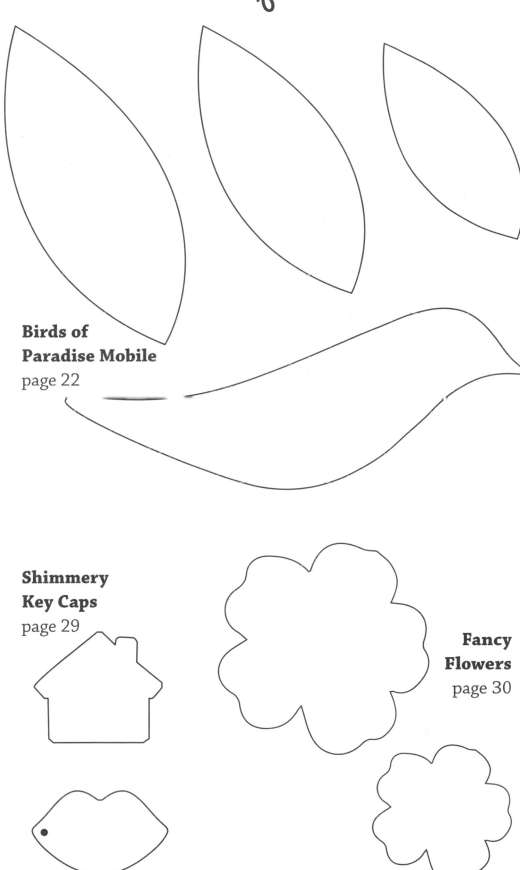

**Birds of
Paradise Mobile**
page 22

**Shimmery
Key Caps**
page 29

**Fancy
Flowers**
page 30

Butterfly Wall Art
page 41